Antique Bottle Finds
in New England

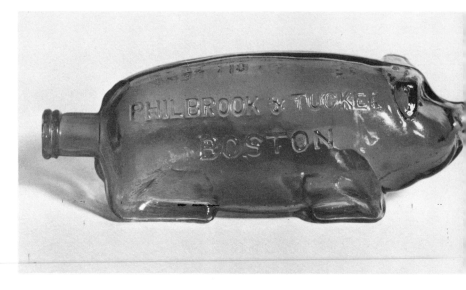

SUFFOLK PIG BITTERS, embossed Philbrook and Tucker, Boston. From Collection of Mrs. George Chamberlain, Jaffrey, New Hampshire.

ANTIQUE
BOTTLE FINDS
in
NEW ENGLAND

Virginia T. Bates
Beverly Chamberlain

NOONE HOUSE
PETERBOROUGH, NEW HAMPSHIRE

Published by William L. Bauhan, Inc., Noone House, Peterborough, New Hampshire (formerly Richard R. Smith, Publishers). Typography by the Cabinet Press, Milford, N. H. and Sim's Press, Peterborough, N. H. Printed at the Murray Printing Company, Forge Village, Mass., and bound at the Colonial Press, Inc., Clinton, Mass.

Acknowledgments

THE AUTHORS wish to express their thanks to those who helped to make this book a reality—especially: George and Hazel Chamberlain of Jaffrey, New Hampshire; Bill and Jessie Hope of Gastonia, North Carolina; Andrew Elder of Dublin, New Hampshire; and to Jorgia Colburn and Fran Doore of Harrisville, New Hampshire.

Our grateful thanks also to Alice, Rick and Fran, who withstood clutter and confusion and general neglect—and to the many friends who stood by us steadfastly during the time it took to prepare and write this book.

We also wish to express our appreciation to Don Maust, editor of *The Antiques Journal,* for permission to reprint portions of our article which appeared in the issue of January-February 1968.

Photographs of the bottles illustrated in this book are by John K. Abbott of Keene, New Hampshire.

VIRGINIA T. BATES
BEVERLY CHAMBERLAIN

Contents

Illustrations

New Hampshire Pharmacy Bottles. *Left to right:* City Pharmacy, Frank
C. Dort, A. M. Doolittle & Co., J. R. Miller & Son, Bullard & Shedd Co.,
Frank C. Dort & Co., Dort & Chandler, B. W. Hodgkins, Aldrich & Dutton.

Anecdotes and Artifacts

How DOES a new hobby start? What does it take to catch on? A consuming interest by many enthusiastic people might be the answer to both questions. Whatever answer you may think of, the fact remains that bottle collecting has most definitely caught on. All over the country, "bottle bugs" are establishing clubs for the study and exchange of old bottles. They are gathering on weekends and holidays for field trips to deserted settlements or cellar holes or ghost towns to dig for old bottles. New books are being placed on the market to help the collector learn about his bottles, and the old bottles themselves are prominently displayed in today's antique shops.

In our own Monadnock region of southwestern New Hampshire, bottle collecting has truly come of age. A few short years ago, collectors discussed their hobby quietly and only among their closest friends. Most of the local inhabitants looked askance at anyone known to be a digger of dumps! Bottle diggers learned to acquire a sense of humor concerning their favorite avocation and a reticence about how they spent their weekends!

Today a change is apparent—the bottle collecting mania, although still a mystery to many, has become a suitable topic of polite conversation. It is quite surprising how many converts

CASE AND GIN BOTTLES. Ginter's and Imperial Gin at the left. Elongated or shingle ridges remaining from the early molds enhance the beauty of the plain case bottles at the right.

are won once they are exposed to a colorful collection of early bottles.

The contents of an old dump may include anything from burial plates to old bones; Stoddard flasks to dead rodents; salt shakers to clam shells! But the tyro is usually single-minded in his search for old bottles, discarding all except the glass—overlooking other lessons that might be learned from his ancestors. Gradually, he may become aware that his vision is expanding, and he finds himself examining with surprise and delight such objects as a hand-wrought iron shovel with an odd-shaped handle; fragments of early china; a pressed-glass salt shaker turning a lovely shade of amethyst; a child's toy fire engine made from cast iron; shards of earthenware. These last caused the authors some excitement on one expedition near home—could they be remnants of Chesham pottery? During the latter part of the 1700's and early 1800's, several potteries flourished in Chesham, New Hampshire, known at that time as Pottersville. Years have passed since the whir of a potter's wheel was heard; but today, Chesham pottery is sought after as a collector's item.

In New England, the bottle-hunting season is short but strenuous. The ground freezes in November and is covered by snow until April or May, at which time the black flies and mosquitoes make their annual reappearance, causing great discomfort to those disturbing their breeding places. The terrain is often rough and uneven. Steep wooded hills are interlaced with brambled fields and crisscrossed by numerous small lakes and streams. Stone walls, built by our hardy ancestors, still serve as property lines and are useful clues when trying to locate abandoned cellar holes. Some of our first bottle finds were made beneath these old walls and, needless to say, they hold a warm spot in our hearts! Many of the old roads leading into deserted properties of the past are little more than footpaths today and anyone who is not partial to exercise will soon give up and return to purchase their bottles from the antique shops! The more hardy souls find these rigorous conditions provide a challenge, adding excitement and adventure to the search—vicissitudes to be overcome with stamina and fortitude.

Digging has succeeded under the most adverse conditions—snow, rain, heat, cold—even by moonlight! On some expeditions we have had the welcome company of a teen-aged son, who—besides having a keen sense of dump detection—disposes of occasional dead mice found in old bottles, while his large dog stands guard against uncongenial reptiles. We have been joined at other times by as many as ten or twelve eager companions of all ages and sizes. Our lives have been endangered by falling, drowning, and exposure—we have even been shot at! (Accidentally, we hope.) There is nothing, however, to replace the sense of adventure and expectancy of starting out on a bright morning for a walk in the woods, or the proud feeling of accomplishment after a hard day's work has unearthed one more treasure for our growing collection of artifacts and old bottles.

This book is devoted to the "middle period" of American bottle collecting. In years, this can be roughly interpreted as starting about 1800 and extending to 1900. We have discussed only blown-in-mold-with-applied-lip bottles, which were blown by lung power into some type of mold with the lips of the bottle finished by hand. No free-blown (early period) or machine-made (late period) bottles have been included.

Nearly all of the examples listed here—from the authors' collections—have been found in or not far from the Monadnock region of southwestern New Hampshire, and they probably represent a good cross-section of old bottles to be found in New England. For those unfamiliar with it, the Monadnock region is located almost in the geographical center of New England and was easily accessible, even in the early nineteenth century, to trade and traffic up and down the Connecticut River Valley, from the seaports of Boston and Portland, and from Albany to the west. Within its boundaries, also, were no less than five early glassworks—to the delight of present-day explorers!

Many collectors prefer to purchase their bottles from antique shops, but there are hundreds more who choose the excitement of reclaiming their bottles from the discarded rubbish of the past. To these heroic reclamation engineers or amateur archaeologists, whichever you prefer, this book is dedicated.

Unembossed Three-Part Mold Bottles. Note mold seam extending below and around the shoulders, and from this another extending up each side of the bottle.

Unembossed Bottles

MANY OF THE EARLIEST blown-in-mold bottles were plain, exhibiting no printing or embossing on the glass. Sometimes a label was pasted to the bottle, or the instructions for use might be tied to the neck. Oftentimes, the contents alone served as the "label." Due to the irregular composition of many early molds, bottles blown in a supposedly rectangular mold are sometimes obtuse in proportion; the neck rising from the body of the bottle often "leans" and the applied lip may drape about the neck in most uneven fashion. Whittle marks, the elongated ridges created by the use of wooden (or cold) molds, are as fascinating as the presence of air bubbles—the transparent, bead-like ovals appearing in much old glass. The bottom of the bottle may display an "open pontil," a sharp, jagged remnant of glass which remained there after the punty rod had been broken away from the container. A bottle with an "improved pontil" would not exhibit this hazardous scar. From the tiniest vial to the many-gallon capacity demijohn, the appealing characteristics of unembossed bottles are limitless.

Three-part and turn mold bottles are examples of the gradually changing methods used in bottle production. As the name implies, bottles blown in a three-part mold exhibit three mold lines, one extending below and around the shoulder of the

UNEMBOSSED TURN-MOLD WINES AND LIQUORS.

bottle and, from this, another on each side of the shoulder extending up the neck of the bottle. Three-part molds evolved from the early "dip" molds. The term "turn mold" describes the method of manufacture whereby either the mold or the bottle was turned after the bottle was formed, leaving no visible seam. Cylindrical impressions and a highly lustrous finish are characteristics of these bottles. When wooden molds became outdated, iron molds lined with paste were used to achieve this glossy appearance which seems to have been popular with the trade. But by far the greatest majority of unembossed bottles found today were blown in two-part molds and are easily identified by the seam running up each side of the bottle.

Observation and study leads to a desire to know what the original contents of the bottle may have been. For anyone seeking this knowledge, an invaluable source book is H. E. Putnam's *Bottle Identification*. Shape and color are the two most useful factors in determining the original use of an un-embossed bottle. Wine or champagne (also called hock) came in tall graceful tapering turn-mold bottles. Liquor bottles with a more bulbous design probably contained whiskey, gin, or bitters. Short, squatty bottles with elongated necks, usually pint size, are connected with brandy and the malt beverages. All of these may be found in shades of aqua, amber, green, and the exceptionally dark-amber and olive-green glass which appears to be black. The term "black glass" is, indeed, used when describing this relatively common color. A deep teal-blue wine or hock bottle would be an uncommon and beautiful find. The taper (or case) bottle is found in olive-green and olive-amber and usually held gin or rum.

Many shapes and sizes went into the production of medicine bottles. Colors included clear, aqua, green, amber, and blue. Clear glass containers were most common; the lovely cobalt relatively uncommon. Many salutary preparations were bottled in dark amber and cobalt vessels since the dark glass was believed to reduce the intensity of light entering the bottle and thus helped to preserve the medicinal contents. Cobalt and amber also seem to have been popular for bottling poisonous preparations and were often combined with a triangular shape and/or a raised motif to aid in identifying the contents in the dark.

Food containers are a delight to many bottle enthusiasts. Flowing designs of twining flowers and delicate leaf patterns enhance the beauty of these early tablewares. Cathedral or Gothic arches grace the panels of many early pickle bottles. Tapered, ringed, and ridged pepper sauce containers were produced in aqua and a vivid, blue-green glass. Rectangular condiment bottles are to be found in brilliant shades of green. Tall, slender turn-mold olive oil bottles, blown in clear glass, are pleasing to the eye.

Fancy perfume or cologne bottles with ground-glass stoppers, ornamented with beaded-rope designs, were products with a feminine flair. Tiny "card colognes" or "ten-cent handkerchiefs" are a charming addition to any collection of old bottles. Hair tonics or "invigorators" were blown in such rare colors as Palmer green and peacock blue. (The buyer would find these to be most enticing even though the ingredients failed to produce the "long flowing locks" advertised!)

Small "sample" bottles are available in nearly all of the

CLEAR GLASS CONTAINERS. *Above:* T. M. Dillingham's, McGee's Horse-head Rye and Bourbon Whiskey, Unembossed horseshoe or coffin flask, Unembossed Union Oval flask, Graduated Nursing Bottle, Walker-Gordon Modified Milk Laboratories, Hemlock Oil, Unembossed sample liquor, Chesebrough Mfg. Co.

BEER, ALE AND WINE BOTTLES. *Below:* Four unembossed examples.

above categories and colors. These miniatures take little room in a collection and are worth the little they take.

Soda water bottles (aqua) are interesting for the various shapes—blob top, Hutchinson type (practically no neck) and the round and pointed bottom variety. These last are said to have been used as ballast on ships sailing from England. Many of the squatty, one-half pint bottles which resemble, in shape, today's beer bottles, originally held soda or spring water. These are nice early bottles having a color range from olive-amber and amber to green and blue, and are considered rare finds in this area.

Every collection of unembossed bottles should include at least one early snuff or blacking bottle. They are usually dark green or amber and, although not easily found, are well worth searching for.

Unembossed flasks are always a happy thought! The subtle differences in shapes, the various sizes, the many beautiful colors lend fascination to these bottles. Variations abound in the types of sheared and applied lips; open and ground pontils. Many seem to have been blown in flint glass. The picturesque names—"shoo-fly," "horseshoe," "coffin," "picnic,"—lend these bottles a romantic aura. In general, the smaller the flask, the more valuable the bottle. Age can be determined by applying the usual rules—mold seams, whittle marks, bubbles, uneven shape, type of pontil, etc. What the original contents may have been is usually a matter for conjecture; we have dug flasks containing everything from chicken fat to varnish! Many of the substances prove difficult to remove—and here a word of caution about cleaning. Many early flasks have thin delicate glass around the shoulders. These shoulders are easily

PICKLE AND SAUCE BOTTLES. *Above:* Square pickle, Seville Packing, H. J. Heinz, Chas. Gulden, Flat peppersauce, John Thomas, D. L. Slade (two examples) and preserve.

PICKLE AND PRESERVE BOTTLES. *Below:* Unembossed examples.

broken by too vigorous shaking or scrubbing. A good long soaking in ammonia water or paint remover, depending on the contents, is recommended. Through sad experience we have learned that patience has, indeed, its own reward!

Last, but not least—ink bottles—the little jewels of the bottle collector's world! Color and shape have been combined in these bottles to give them a special appeal to all collectors. The small cone or pyramidal shapes in aqua, amber, green, and cobalt are delightful. The earlier eight and twelve-sided cones have an added interest because of open pontils, whittle marks, and bubbles. Early cylindrical containers with pinched pouring spouts are irresistible in the old colors of olive-green and amber. These larger ink bottles are rare finds because of their size. Although they are not listed here, early stone-ware and pottery ink bottles are much to be desired. Large or small, colored or clear, rare or common—ink bottles add sparkle and zest to the old bottle collection.

Embossed Bottles

KEY TO ABBREVIATIONS
Used In Tables

Amb	=	Amber	Grn	=	Green
Aq	=	Aqua	L	=	Left
B	=	Back	OG	=	Olive Green
Bl	=	Blue	OP	=	Open Pontil
Bs	=	Base	Ov	=	Oval
Btm	=	Bottom	Pnl	=	Pnl
Case	=	Taper Square	R	=	Right
Cl	=	Clear	Rect	=	Rectangular
Cob	=	Cobalt	SCA	=	Sun-colored Amethyst
Cone	=	Pyramidal	Shl	=	Shoulder
Cyl	=	Cylindrical	SL	=	Sheared Lip
F	=	Front	Sq	=	Square
Flsk	=	Flask	ST	=	Screw Top

Unless otherwise indicated,
EMBOSSING appears on front
of bottle.

¶ = Photograph of bottle

(#) = Notes on Bottles, pp. 68, 69.

EMBOSSING	TYPE	SHAPE	COLOR	HGT.	$ VAL.
<u>A</u>					
A. B. CO. (Btm)	Beer	Cyl	Aq-Amb	9	1 - 2
A. B. G. M. CO. (Btm)	Beer	Cyl	Aq	9 1/2	1 - 2
¶ C. W. ABBOTT & CO. BALTIMORE (Shld) (Same as above) (Btm)	Bitt	Cyl	Amb	8	4 - 7
ABSORBINE $2.00 PER BOTTLE MFG. BY W. F. YOUNG, P. D. F. SPRINGFIELD, MASS.	Med.	Rect	Amb	7 1/2	2 - 4
ALBOLENE (REGISTERED)	Hshld	Sq	Cl	8 1/4	1 - 2
¶ ALDRICH & DUTTON DRUGGISTS KEENE, N. H.	Med	Rect	Cl	5	1 - 2
ARMOURS VIGORAL CHICAGO	Hshld	Sq	Amb	2 1/2	1 - 2
DR. SETH ARNOLD'S (L) CAP BALSAM 7D (R)	Med	Rect	Cl	4 1/2	1 - 3
ATHLETIC CLUB	Med	Flsk	Cl	8 1/2	1 - 2
¶ ATWOOD'S JAUNDICE BITTERS MOSES ATWOOD GEORGETOWN, MASS.	Bitt	12 Panel Cyl	Aq	6	5 - 7
ATWOOD'S JAUNDICE BITTERS FORMERLY MADE BY MOSES ATWOOD GEORGETOWN, MASS.	Bitt	12 Panel Cyl	Aq	6	4 - 6
¶ AUSTENS' FOREST FLOWER COLOGNE W. J. AUSTEN & CO. OSWEGO, N. Y.	Cosm	Cyl	Cl	2 1/2	1 - 2

EMBOSSING	TYPE	SHAPE	COLOR	HGT.	$ VAL.
B					
B.A.6 (Btm)	Beer	Cyl	Amb	9	3 - 5
ACID LINE MANUFACTURED BY E.G.BADGER & SONS COMPANY BOSTON, MASS. U.S.A.	Hshld	Cyl	Aq	6	1 - 3
BAKER'S FLAVORING EXTRACTS BAKER EXTRACT CO. STRENGTH & PURITY (R) FULL MEASURE (L)	Food	Rect	Cl	6 4 3/4	1 - 2
BAKER'S FLORIDA WATER PORTLAND	Cosm	Cyl	Aq	7	2 - 4
JNO. T. BARBEE & CO. DISTILLERS LOUISVILLE, KY.	Liq	Flsk	Cl	7 1/4	2 - 3
E.G.BARTHEL & CO. (Mono EGB&CO) GARDNER, MASS.	Beer	Cyl	Cl	9 1/2	2 - 4
S. BARTLETT LOWELL, MASS. (F) THIS BOTTLE NOT TO BE SOLD (B)	Beer	Cyl	Aq	9 1/4	2 - 4
BEARS OIL (SL) (OP)	Med	Rect	Aq	3	3 - 4
¶ J.E.BILLINGS & CO. PITTSFIELD, MASS. 1873 (B)	Soda	Cyl	Aq	7 1/2	3 - 5
BINNINGERS OLD DOMINION (F) WHEAT TONIC (L) A.M.BINNINGER & CO. (B) NO. 19 BROAD ST. N.Y. (R)	Med	Sq	Amb	10	10-12

EMBOSSED BITTERS BOTTLES. *Left to right:* Lash's Bitters, Dr. Flint's Quaker Bitters, Dr. Langley's Root & Herb Bitters, Dr. Townsend's Sarsaparilla, Atwood's Jaundice Bitters.

EMBOSSING	TYPE	SHAPE	COLOR	HGT.	$ VAL.
BIXBY (Btm)	Hshld	Cone	Cl	2 1/2	1 - 2
(#)G.O. BLAKE'S RYE & BOUR WHISKEY ADAMS TAYLOR CO. PROPRIETORS BOSTON & LOUISVILLE (2 Barrels, 1 resting on other, initials "SOB" in end of one.)	Liq	Cyl	Cl	12	2 - 4
BROMO CAFFEINE	Med	Cyl	Bl	3 1/4	2 - 3
BROMO SELTZER EMERSON DRUG CO. BALTIMORE, MD.	Med	Cyl	Cob	4	1 - 2
¶ F. BROWN'S (F) ESS OF JAMAICA GINGER PHILADA (OP)	Med	Ov	Aq	7 1/2	3 - 4
BRYANT'S ROOT BEER (F) MANUFACTURED BY WILLIAMS DAVIS BROOKS & CO. (B) THIS BOTTLE MAKES FIVE GALLONS (L) DETROIT, MICH. (R)	Food	Rect	Aq	4 1/2	1 - 2
BRYANT'S ROOT BEER (F) DETROIT, MICH. (R) THIS BOTTLE MAKES FIVE GALLONS (L)	Food	Rect	Amb	4 1/2	1 - 2
BUFFALO LITHIA SPRING WATER NATURES MATERIA MEDICA (Woman holding pitcher) TRADE MARK PAT.	Med	Cyl	Aq	10	7 - 9
(#)BULLARD & FOSTER PHARMACISTS		Rect	Cl	5 1/2	
KEENE, N.H.	Med	Ov	Cl	5	1 - 2
¶ BULLARD & SHEDD CO. PHARMACISTS KEENE, N.H. (F)				6 1/2 5 1/2 4 3/4	
MARVEL (Btm)	Med	Ov	Cl	3 3/4	1 - 2

EMBOSSING	TYPE	SHAPE	COLOR	HGT.	$ VAL.
BULLOCK & GRENSHAW	Med	Rect	Cl	4	1 - 2
¶ BURBANK MFG. CO. BOSTON, MASS. U.S.A.	Hshld	Rect	Aq	4 3/4	1 - 3
BURKHARDT BREWING CO. BOSTON TRADE MARK "IN UNION IS STRENGTH" REGISTERED	Beer	Cyl	Amb	9 3/4	2 - 4
BURNETT BOSTON	Hshld	Flsk	Aq	6 1/2	1 - 2
BURNETT BOSTON	Hshld	Cyl	Aq	7 1/2	1 - 2
BURNETTS (L) BOSTON (R)	Hshld	Rect	Cl	4 1/2	1 - 2

C

EMBOSSING	TYPE	SHAPE	COLOR	HGT.	$ VAL.
CABOT'S SULPHO-NAPTHOL TRADE MARK REG.U.S.PAT.OF. BOSTON, MASS. USA	Hshld	Cyl	Amb	9	1 - 3
CABOT'S SULPHO-NAPTHOL BOSTON, MASS. U.S.A.	Hshld	Rect	Amb	4 1/4 6	1 - 3
M. CARNEY & CO. LAWRENCE, MASS. 53 & 55 HAMPSHIRE ST. 421 & 423 COMMON ST. (F) THIS BOTTLE NOT TO BE SOLD (Bs)	Beer	Cyl	Cl	9	2 - 4
CARTERS 1897 (Btm)	Ink	Cone	Aq	2 1/4	2 - 4
CARTER'S 62 (Btm)	Ink	Cone	Aq	2 1/2	2 - 4
¶ CARTER'S (Shld) PAT.FEB.14,'99 (Btm)	Ink	Cyl	Grn	7 1/2	3 - 4

EMBOSSING	TYPE	SHAPE	COLOR	HGT.	$ VAL.
¶ CARTER'S MADE IN U.S.A. (Shld) (Cathedral windows etched around base) PAT. FEB. 14-99 (Btm)	Ink	Cyl	Aq	9 1/2	4 - 6
CARTER'S FULL PINT (Bs) MADE IN U.S.A. (Btm)	Ink	Cyl	Aq	7 1/2	2 - 5
CARTER'S 1897 MADE IN U.S.A. (Btm)	Ink	Cone	Amb	2 1/2	3 - 5
¶ CARTER'S 77 (Btm)	Ink	Cone	Cob	2 1/2	3 - 5
¶ CAW'S INK NEW YORK	Ink	Sq	Aq	2 1/4	2 - 3
C.B.BRO M (Btm)	Food	Cyl	Aq	8	1 - 3
C.B.C. LYNN, MASS. (F) REGISTERED (B) B24 (Btm)	Soda	Cyl	Aq	7	2 - 5
CELEBRATED CLICQUOT-CLUB TRADE MARK REG. BEVERAGES MADE IN AMERICA	Soda	Cyl	Cl Aq	9 1/2	1 - 3
¶ CHAMBERLAIN'S COLIC CHOLLRA DIARRHER REMEDY (F) CHAMBERLAIN MED.CO. (R) DES MOINES, IA.,U.S.A. (L)	Med	Rec	Aq	4 1/2	2 - 3
¶ CHAMBERLAIN'S COUGH REMEDY (F) CHAMBERLAIN MED. CO. (R) DES MOINES IA. USA (L)	Med	Rect	Aq	5 1/2	1 - 3
CHARLES & CO. NEW YORK	Liq	Cyl	Amb	11 3/4	3 - 6
G.S.CHENEY & CO. BOSTON, MASS.	Hshld	Rect	Aq	9 1/2	1 - 3

EMBOSSING	TYPE	SHAPE	COLOR	HGT.	$ VAL.
¶ CHESEBROUGH MFG. CO. VASELINE	Med	Cyl	Cl	3	1 - 2
OTIS CLAPP & SONS MALT AND COD LIVER OIL COMPOUND	Med	Rect	Amb	7 1/2	2 - 4
COCA MARIANI PARIS (F) COCA MARIANI E FRANCE (Btm)	Liq	Grn	Cyl	9	3 - 6
C. N. COLBURN & CO. 91 W. PEARL ST. NASHUA, N. H. REGISTERED (F) THIS BOTTLE NOT TO BE SOLD (Bs)	Beer	Cyl	Cl	9	2 - 4
G. W. COLE CO. (R) THREE IN ONE (L)	Hshld	Rect	Aq	5 1/4	1 - 2
¶ COLGATE & CO. PERFUMERS NEW YORK	Cosm	Cyl	Cl	2 1/2	1 - 3
COLTS FOOT EXPECTORANT	Med	Rect	Aq	6 1/2	1 - 3
CONTINENTAL BREWING CO. BOSTON (B)	Beer	Cyl	Amb	9 1/2	2 - 5
E. A. COUDRAY A. A. PARIS	Cosm	Cyl	Cl	7 1/2	1 - 2
E. T. COWDREY CO. BOSTON (Btm)	Food	Cyl	Cl	6	1 - 2
¶ CPC (Monogram)	Ink	Rnd	Aq	3	2 - 4
¶ DR. CUMMING'S VEGETINE	Med	Ov	Aq	9 1/2	3 - 5
CURTIS & MOORE FRUIT SYRUPS BOSTON, MASS.	Food	Sq	Cl	10	2 - 3

"Cure-alls" Embossed with Enticing Names. *Back row, left to right:* Dr. Cummings Vegetine, The Great Dr. Kilmer's Swamp-Root, Dr. Kilmer's Swamp-Root, Dana's Sarsaparilla, Groder's Botanic Dyspepsia Syrup, Tuttle's Elixir, Healy & Bigelow's Kickapoo Indian Oil. *Front row:* Chamberlain's Cough Remedy, Chamberlain's Colic Chollra Diarrher Remedy, F. Brown's Jamaica Ginger (open pontil), Dr. Kilmer's Swamp-Root and Kidney Remedy (sample), Kodol Nerve Tonic (sample), Free Sample Blood Wine, Unembossed sample, Rev. N. H. Downs' Vegetable Balsamic Elixir, Kemps Balsam, Doc. T. Marshall's Snuff.

EMBOSSING	TYPE	SHAPE	COLOR	HGT.	$ VAL.
THE CUTICURA SYSTEM OF CURING CONSTITUTIONAL HUMORS (F) ORIGINATED BY WEEKS & POTTER BOSTON (B)	Med	Sq	Aq	9	2 - 4
CUTICURA TREATMENT FOR AFFECTIONS OF THE SKIN (F) POTTER DRUG & CHEMICAL CORP. BOSTON, U.S.A. (B)	Med	Sq	Aq	9 1/4	2 - 4

<u>D</u>

EMBOSSING	TYPE	SHAPE	COLOR	HGT.	$ VAL.
C. DAMSCHINSKY LIQUID HAIR DYE NEW YORK	Cosm	Rect	Aq	3 1/2	2 - 4
¶ DANA'S SARSAPARILLA	Med	Rect	Aq	9	2 - 4
DANA'S SARSAPARILLA MAINE (R) BELFAST (L)	Med	Rect	Aq	8 1/2	2 - 4
SAMPLE BLOOD WINE (F) WORCESTER, MASS. (L) THE LOUIS DAUDELIN CO. (R)	Med	Rect	Cl	3 1/2	2 - 3
¶ BLOOD WINE SAMPLE BOTTLE THE LOUIS DAUDELIN CO. (R) WORCESTER, MASS. (L)	Med	Rect	Cl	3 1/4	2 - 3
#) ¶ DAVIS (F) VEGETABLE (R) PAINKILLER (L)	Med	Rect	Aq	6	1 - 3
DeMERIDOR'S LIQUID BEAUTY POWDER	Cosm	Rect	Cl	5	1 - 2
E.C.DeWITT & CO. (R) CHICAGO U.S.A. (L) ONE MINUTE COUGH CURE (B)	Med	Rect	Aq	5 1/2	1 - 3
#) ¶ T.M.DILLINGHAM'S PAT. APR 7, 1896 (Btm)		Cyl	SCA	11	5 - 8

EMBOSSING	TYPE	SHAPE	COLOR	HGT.	$ VAL.
DIOXOGEN (Bs F) THE OAKLAND CHEMICAL COMP'Y (B)	Hshld	Cyl	Amb	7	1 - 3
¶ FRANK C. DORT & CO. DRUGGISTS, KEENE, N.H.	Med	Sq	Cl	3 5 1/2	1 - 2
(#) ¶ DORT & CHANDLER DRUGGISTS ESTLB. 1850 KEENE, N.H.	Med	Ov	Cl	5	1 - 2
¶ REV. N.H. DOWNS' VEGETABLE BALSAMIC ELIXIR	Med	12 Panel Cyl	Aq	4 1/2	2 - 4
THE DUFFY MALT WHISKEY CO. ROCHESTER, N.Y. U.S.A. (Mono DMW CO) ONE FIFTH GALLON (B) PAT'D AUG 24 1886 (Btm)	Liq	Cyl	Amb	10	3 - 5
¶ S.O. DUNBAR TAUNTON MASS.	Ink	Cyl	Aq	5 3/4	2 - 4
DURKEE & CO. SAUCE	Food	Cyl	Aq	9	1 - 2
E					
EASTMAN/ROCHESTER, N.Y. 1 OZ. 2 OZ. 3 OZ 4 OZ.	Hshld	Rect	Cl	5	1 - 3
¶ EAU DE COLOGNE NO. 04711	Cosm	Panel Sq	Cl	4 1/2	1 - 3
C.H. EDDY & CO. (Monogram) BRATTLEBORO, VT.	Soda Beer	Cyl	Cl	9 1/2	1 - 2
C.H. EDDY & CO. BRATTLEBORO, VT. REGISTERED	Soda Beer	Cyl	Cl	8	1 - 2

EMBOSSING	TYPE	SHAPE	COLOR	HGT.	$ VAL.
ELY'S CREAM BALM ELY BRO'S OWEGO, N.Y. CATARRH (L) HAY FEVER (R)	Med	Rect	Amb	3	2 - 3
¶ EVERETT & BARRONS SHOE DRESSINGS PROVIDENCE, R.I. USA	Hshld	Rect	Aq	5 1/2	2 - 3

F

EMBOSSING	TYPE	SHAPE	COLOR	HGT.	$ VAL.
¶ M. FAIRBANKS & CO. BOSTON	Soda	Cyl	Aq	7 1/2	2 - 4
¶ FARLEY'S INK	Ink	6 Pnl	Amb	4	15-25
FARLEY'S INK	Ink	6 Pnl	Amb	8 3/4	20-25
FARWELL'S QUINCE CREAM EAST CAMBRIDGE	Cosm	Rect	Cl	5	1 - 3
FATHER JOHN'S MEDICINE LOWELL, MASS.	Med	Rect	Amb	7 1/2	2 - 4
¶ FELLOWS & CO. CHEMISTS ST.JOHN, N.B.	Hshld	Ov	Aq	8	1 - 3
DRS. S.S.FITCH & SON 714 BROADWAY NEW YORK	Med	Ov Flsk	Aq	5	3 - 5
¶ DR. FLINT'S QUAKER BITTERS QUAKERS (B) DR. FLINT'S (R) PROVIDENCE, R.I. (L)	Bitt	Rect	Aq	9	12-15
FOREST FLOWER COLOGNE W.J.AUSTIN & CO. OSWEGO, N.Y.	Cosm	Cyl	Cl	3	1 - 2
FOLEY'S HONEY AND TAR FOLEY & CO. CHICAGO, U.S.A.	Med	Rec	Aq	5 1/2	1 - 2

CHEMICAL AND HOUSEHOLD CONTAINERS. *Above:* Aqua Chemical, Vici Leather Dressing, Burbank Mfg., Gilt Edge Dressing, Everett & Barrons Shoe Dressing, Acme Blacking, Fellow's & Co. Chemists.

MEDICINES AND TONICS. *Left, above:* Two unembossed sample bottles, Perry Davis Pain Killer, Superior Hair Oil, Wyoming Catarrh Cure. *Left, below:* Two wooden medicine containers, Pint size Warranted Flask, Unembossed picnic or shoo-fly flask.

EMBOSSING	TYPE	SHAPE	COLOR	HGT.	$ VAL.
FOLEY'S KIDNEY & BLADDER REMEDY	Med	Rect	Amb	9 1/2	2 - 4
GEO. L. FORBUSH APOTHECARY PETERBORO, N.H. PAT'D MAY 15, 88 (Btm)	Med	Rect	Cl	4 1/4	1 - 2
FRENCH REMEDY FOR COLDS THROAT & LUNG TROUBLES (F) EDWARD HEFFERNAN NO. 88 PORTLAND ST. BOSTON, MASS. NEW ENGLAND AGENT (B)	Med	Sq	Cl	11 1/4	3 - 5
GEO. C. FRYE PORTLAND ME. (Mortor & pestle with Eucolyptis leaves)	Med	Rect	Cl	4 1/4	1 - 3
GEORGE C. FRYE PORTLAND ME.	Med	Rect	Cl	6	1 - 2
FULL PINT (B) (Taken from what was left of label, which read "Dickenson's Witch Hazel, Double Distilled, Essex, Conn., E.E.Dickinson & Co. Contains Alcohol 15% Available locally & indicated for the relief of rheumatism, neuralgia, bruises, piles, hemorrhage, etc.	Med	Ov Flsk	Cl	8 1/2	2 - 3
FULL QUART	Liq	Cyl	Aq	10 1/2	3 - 5
G.					
R.W.GARDNER NEW YORK (acid line etched)	Hshld	Cyl	Cl	7	1 - 3
¶ GILT EDGE DRESSING (7 point Star) (F) (Star design all over bottle) PAT. MAY 10,1880 (Btm)	Hshld	Cyl	Aq	4	3 - 5

EMBOSSING	TYPE	SHAPE	COLOR	HGT.	$ VAL.
¶ GINTER CO. IMPORTERS BOSTON, MASS. CONTENTS 16 OZ. THE GINTER CO. REGISTERED 1250 (Btm)	Liq	Case	Grn	8 1/2	4 - 8
GLENBROOK DISTILLING CO. BOSTON, MASS. SEND FOR OUR CATALOGUE	Liq	Rect Flsk	Cl	6 1/2	2 - 4
GLENDALE SPRING CO. EVERETT, MASS. (F) THIS BOTTLE NOT TO BE SOLD (B)	Soda	Cyl	Aq	7	2 - 4
GLYCO-THYMOLINE	Med	Sq	Cl	2	1 - 2
GODEFROY ST. LOUIS, MO. MEXICO, DF. MEX.	Med	Rect	Cl	6	1 - 2
GOLDEN TREE PINE HONEY 4 FLUID OUNCES WEIGHT 5 OUNCES (F) NEW ENGLAND MAPLE SYRUP COMPANY/BOSTON (B)　(ST)	Food	Cyl	Cl	5 1/2	1 - 2
GORDAK'S DROPS　(OP)	Med	Cyl	Aq	5	3 - 5
GORDON'S DRY GIN LONDON, ENGLAND (Boar's head faces left) (Btm)	Liq	Sq	Aq	8 1/2	2 - 4
¶ THE GRADUATED NURSING BOTTLE (F) F.&W. (B) TABLESPOON/OUNCE (B) (Numerals in line under each)	Food	Ov	Cl	6 1/2	2 - 4
GRAND UNION CO. (Mono ETA in insignia) GRAND UNION TEA CO. (R) (Same) (L)	Hshld	Rect	Cl	5	1 - 2
GRAND UNION TEA COMPANY	Hshld	Rect	Cl	7	1 - 2

EMBOSSING	TYPE	SHAPE	COLOR	HGT.	$ VAL.
C. H. GRAVES & SONS BOSTON, MASS.	Liq	Cyl	Amb	9 3/4	4 - 6
E. E. GRAY CO. IMPORTERS AND WHOLESALE GROCERS BOSTON, MASS. USA	Liq	Rect Flsk	Cl	10	2 - 4
GEO. E. GREENE PHARMACISTS BRATTLEBORO (F) PAT. JAN 24 88 (Btm)	Med	Ov	Cl	5 1/4	1 - 2
¶ GRODER'S BOTANIC DYSPEPSIA SYRUP (F) U. S. A. (R) WATERVILLE, ME. (L)	Med	Rect	Aq	9	3 - 5
¶ CHARLES GULDEN (Btm)	Food	Cyl * * 4 1" bulbous sections	Cl	5 1/2 9 1/4	3 - 5
CHARLES GULDEN NEW YORK (Btm)	Food	Cyl	Cl	9 1/2	1 - 2
N. G. GURNSEY & CO. KEENE, N. H.	Soda	Cyl	Cl	8	1 - 2

H

EMBOSSING	TYPE	SHAPE	COLOR	HGT.	$ VAL.
M. A. HANIGAN & CO. FITCHBURG, MASS. REGISTERED (Fancy Script)	Beer	Cyl	Aq	9	2 - 4
E. HARTSHORN & SONS BOSTON, MASS. EST. 1850	Med	Rect	Cl	4 3/4	1 - 2
E. HARTSHORN & SONS BOSTON (Mono)	Med	Rect	Aq	7	1 - 2
VINCENT HATHAWAY & CO. BOSTON TRADE MARK REGISTERED	Soda	Cyl	Cl	8 1/4	1 - 2

ORNAMENTED PERFUME AND COLOGNES. *Above:* Five unembossed cosmetics. *Below:* Unembossed cosmetic, Eau de Cologne, Ed. Pinard Paris, Colgate (ground glass stopper), Austen's Forest Flower.

EMBOSSING	TYPE	SHAPE	COLOR	HGT.	$ VAL.
HAYNER WHISKEY DISTILLERY TROY, OHIO DESIGN PATENTED NOV. 30TH, 1897 (Btm)	Liq	Cyl	Cl	11 1/2	2 - 3
DR. HAYNES ARABIAN BALSAM MORGAN & SONS PROVIDENCE, R.I.	Med	12 Panel Cyl	Aq	4 1/4	2 - 4
HAZELTINE & CO. (L) PISO'S & CO. (R) FOR CONSUMPTION (F)	Med	Rect	Aq	5 1/4	2 - 4
¶ HEALY & BIGELOW'S KICKAPOO INDIAN OIL	Med	Cyl	Aq	5 1/2	2 - 4
THE HEFFRON CO. SYRACUSE N.Y.	Med	Cyl	Cl	4	1 - 2
H.J.HEINZ CO. (Btm)	Food	Cyl	Cl	8	1 - 2
¶ H.J.HEINZ CO. PITTSBURGH, U.S.A. (Btm)	Food	Cyl	Cl	7 1/2	1 - 2
¶ HEMLOCK OIL CO. DERRY N.H.	Med	Sq	Cl	5	2 - 4
¶ G.F.HEWITT BOSTON MASS	Soda	Cyl	Aq	9	3 - 5
HINCKEL BREWING CO. BOSTON, MASS. REGISTERED	Beer	Cyl	Cl	9	2 - 4
¶ HIRES (Btm)	Soda	Cyl	Aq	9 1/4	1 - 3

EMBOSSING	TYPE	SHAPE	COLOR	HGT.	$ VAL.
HIRES ROOTBEER (F) PHILADELPHIA U.S.A. (R) MAKES 5 GALLONS OF A DELICIOUS DRINK (L) MANUFACTURED BY THE CHARLES E.HIRES CO. (B)	Food	Sq	Aq	4 1/2	1 - 2
¶ CITY PHARMACY HITCHCOCK & HODGKINS KEENE, N.H.	Med	Rect	Cl	3 1/2	1 - 2
¶ B.W.HODGKINS REGISTERED PHARMACIST KEENE, N.H. A.M.F. (Bs)	Med	Ov	Cl	4 3/4	1 - 2
JOHANN HOFF	Malt	Cyl	OG	7 3/4	3 - 5
REGISTERED HONEST ONE QUART	Liq	Rect Flsk	Cl	10 1/2	1 - 2
HOODS SARSA/PARILLA LOWELL, MASS. (R) C.I.HOOD & CO. (L) APOTHECARIES (B)	Med	Rect	Aq	9	2 - 4
HOOD'S SARSAPARILLA LOWELL, MASS. (R) C.I.HOOD & CO. (L)	Med	Rect	Aq	9	2 - 4
HOODS TOOTH POWDER C.I.HOOD & CO. LOWELL, MASS.	Cosm	Ov	Cl	3 1/2	1 - 3
HORLICK'S MALTED MILK RACINE, WIS. USA LONDON, ENG. (ST)	Food	Cyl	Aq	5	1 - 3
¶ DR. J. HOSTETTER'S STOMACH BITTERS L.C.CO. #76 (Btm)	Bitt	Sq	Amb	8 1/2	6 - 8

EMBOSSING	TYPE	SHAPE	COLOR	HGT.	$ VAL.
DR. J. HOSTETTER'S STOMACH BITTERS L&W (Btm)	Bitt	Sq	Amb	8 1/2	8-10
HOWARD'S VEGETABLE (F) CANCER AND CANKER SYRUP (B)	Med	Rect	Amb	8 1/2	10-20
E.W.HOYT & CO. HOYTS GERMAN COLOGNE LOWELL, MASS.	Cosm	Cyl	Cl	3 3/4 7 1/4	1 - 2 2 - 4
RICHARD HUDNUT NEW YORK PARIS (Btm)	Cosm	6 Panel	Cl	7	1 - 2
H.W.HUGULEY CO. 134 CANAL ST. BOSTON MASS.	Liq	Rect Flsk	Cl	10	2 - 4
H.W.HUGULEY CO. 134 CANAL ST. BOSTON	Liq	(Long, bulbous neck) Sq	Cl	10 1/2	2 - 4
HUMPHREY'S HOMEO MED.CO. NEW YORK	Med	Sq	Amb	2 1/2	2 - 4
HYGEIA BREWING CO. (Mono HB) PASSAIC, N.J. REGISTERED THIS BOTTLE NOT TO BE SOLD	Beer	Cyl	Aq	9	2 - 4
I					
DR. H.A.INGRAMS NERVINE PAIN EXTR. (R)	Med	Rect	Aq	4 3/4	1 - 2
¶ IMPERIAL GIN (F) H.H.S. & CO. (B) L & W (Btm)	Liq	Case	Amb	9 1/2	10-15
J					
JSP (Mono) (F)	Malt	Cyl	Grn	9	3 - 5

EMBOSSING	TYPE	SHAPE	COLOR	HGT.	$ VAL.
DR. STEPHEN JEWETT (R) RINDGE, N.H. (L) CELEBRATED HEALTH RESTORING BITTERS (F)　(OP)	Bitt	Rect	Aq	7 1/2	15-20
JOHNSON'S AMERICAN ANODYNE LINIMENT	Med	12 Panel	Aq	4 1/2	2 - 4
THE JOYCE CO. WINES & LIQUORS COR CENTRAL & MIDDLE STS. LOWELL, MASS.	Liq	Rect Flsk	Cl	7	2 - 4

K

EMBOSSING	TYPE	SHAPE	COLOR	HGT.	$ VAL.
J.T.KEEFE 359 & 361 MAIN ST. FITCHBURG, MASS. (F) REGISTERED (Bs)	Soda/ Beer	Cyl	Cl	9 1/2	2 - 4
P.K.KELLEY LOWELL, MASS.	Soda	Cyl	Cl	9	1 - 2
¶ KEMPS BALSAM	Med	Ov	Cl	2 3/4	1 - 2
KERKOFF (Mono) KD PARIS FRANCE	Cosm	Rect	Aq	5	1 - 2
¶ THE GREAT DR. KILMER'S SWAMP ROOT KIDNEY LIVER AND BLADDER CURE SPECIFIC (F) DR. KILMER & CO. (R) BINGHAMPTON, N.Y. (L)	Med	Rect	Aq	8	3 - 4
¶ DR. KILMER'S SWAMP-ROOT KIDNEY REMEDY BINGHAMPTON, N.Y. (Sample)	Med	Cyl	Aq	4 1/4	2 - 3
DR. KING'S NEW DISCOVERY FOR CONSUMPTION (F) H.E.BUCKLEN & CO. (R) CHICAGO, ILL. (L)	Med	Rect	Aq	6 1/2 8	1 - 3

BLOB-TOP SODAS WITH TWO BALLAST BOTTLES IN FOREGROUND. *Left to right:* Unembossed soda, Hires, J. E. Billings & Co., G. F. Hewitt, M. Fairbanks & Co., Pfaff & Hansom, Unembossed soda.

Sodas and Beers. Unembossed amber soda or beer, E. Wagner, Mountain Spring Brewing, Bunker Hill Lager, Unembossed amber soda or beer, Unembossed green soda or beer.

EMBOSSING	TYPE	SHAPE	COLOR	HGT.	$ VAL.
C.A.KING PURE MALT DEPT. BOSTON, MASS. (Btm)	Malt	Cyl	Amb	8 1/2	2 - 4
¶ KODOL NERVE TONIC FREE SAMPLE (F) E.G.DeWITT & CO. CHICAGO (Btm)	Med	Cyl	Aq	3 1/2	2 - 4

<u>L</u>

EMBOSSING	TYPE	SHAPE	COLOR	HGT.	$ VAL.
LARABEE'S LINAMENT	Med	Sq	Cyl	5 & 6	1 - 2
LAKIN'S (F) KOLONE (B) HEDAKE (L) BOSTON (R)	Med	Sq	Cl	2	1 - 3
¶ DR. LANGLEY'S ROOT & HERB BITTERS 76 UNION ST. BOSTON	Bitt	Cyl	Grn	7	12-20
¶ DR. LANGLEY'S ROOT & HERB BITTERS	Bitt	Cyl	Aq	6	6 - 8
LARKIN CO. BUFFALO (Mono LD)	Hshld	Cyl	Cl	5 1/2	1 - 2
LARKIN CO. BUFFALO (Mono LC)	Hshld	Rect	Cl	6	1 - 2
LARKIN CO. BUFFALO TOILET WATER	Cosm	Cyl	Cl	6 3/4	1 - 2
LARKIN CO. BUFFALO DERMA BALM	Cosm	Sq	Cl	4 3/4	1 - 2

EMBOSSING	TYPE	SHAPE	COLOR	HGT.	$ VAL.
LARKIN SOAP CO. (R) BUFFALO, N.Y. (L) (Mono LSCO) (F)	Hshld	Rect	Cl	5	1 - 2
LARKIN SOAP CO. (F) C.P.GLYCERINE #4 (B)	Hshld	Cyl	Cl	5 3/4	1 - 2
¶ LASH'S BITTERS CO. NEW YORK-CHICAGO SAN FRANCISCO	Bitt	Cyl	Cl	11	5 - 8
LAVIS & CROWLEY 758-760 WASHINGTON ST. BOSTON, MASS.	Liq	Rect Flsk	Cl	6 3/4	2 - 4
LEMP ST. LOUIS (F) AB CO. (Btm)	Beer	Cyl	Aq	9	1 - 2
DR. LESURE'S COLIC CURE #447 (Btm)	Med	Rect	Cl	3 3/4	2 - 3
(#)DR. LESURE'S COLIC CURE NO. 2	Med	Sq	Cl	3 1/2	2 - 3
DR. LESURE'S LINAMENT	Med	Rect	Cl	6	2 - 3
(#)O. LETTENMAYER KEENE N.H.	Soda	Cyl	Aq	7	3 - 5
LIQUOZONE MANUFACTURED ONLY BY THE LIQUID OZONE CO. CHICAGO, U.S.A.	Hshld	Cyl	Amb	6	1 - 3

M .

EMBOSSING	TYPE	SHAPE	COLOR	HGT.	$ VAL.
¶ McGEE'S HORSEHEAD RYE & BOURBON WHISKIES (Horse's Head in circle)	Liq	Rect Flsk	Cl	8 1/2	4 - 8

EMBOSSING	TYPE	SHAPE	COLOR	HGT.	$ VAL.
THE E. MAAS BOTTLING CO. 931 3rd AVE. N.Y. REGISTERED (F) THIS BOTTLE NOT TO BE SOLD (B)	Soda/ Beer	Cyl	Aq	9	2 - 4
THE MALTINE MFG. CO. NEW YORK	Med	Rect	Amb	6 1/2	2 - 4
THE MALTINE MFG. CO. CHEMISTS NEW YORK	Med	Rect	Amb	7 3/4	2 - 5
¶ DOC. T. MARSHALL'S (R) SNUFF (L)	Med	Rect	Aq	3 1/4	3 - 4
MASON'S PATENT NOV. 30th 1858 (F) (Mono FJCCO) (B) (ST)	Hshld	1 Qt. Jar Cyl	Aq	7 1/2	2 - 3
MASON'S (Mono FJCCO) PATENT NOV. 30th 1858 (ST)	Hshld	1 & 2 Qt. Jar Cyl	Aq	7 1/4 9	3 - 5
MASSACHUSETTS BREWERIES CO. BOSTON (Btm)	Beer	Cyl	Amb	9 3/4	2 - 5
MELLINS INFANT FOODS DOLIBER GOODALE CO. BOSTON (Glass Top)	Food	Cyl	Aq	6 1/2	1 - 3
¶ MELLINS FOOD (F) FREE SAMPLE (B)	Food	Cyl	Aq	3 3/4	1 - 3
MELVIN & BADGER APOTHECARIES BOSTON	Med	Sq	Cl	9 3/4	2 - 4
MELVIN & BADGER BOSTON (F) METCALF CO. (Btm)	Med	Cyl	Cl	3 3/4	1 - 2

EMBOSSING	TYPE	SHAPE	COLOR	HGT.	$ VAL.
JOHN MEYER CHEMISTS MT. CLEMENS MICH. (Btm)	Hshld	Cyl	Amb	9 1/4	3 - 4
MILLER'S	Cosm	Rect	Cl	3	1 - 2
MILLER'S GAMECOCK WHISKEY BOSTON	Liq	Ov Flsk	Aq	8 1/2	3 - 5
DR. J. MILLER'S VEGETABLE EXPECTORANT E. MORGAN & SONS PROVIDENCE, R.I.	Med	12 Panel Cyl	Cl	5 3/4	2 - 4
¶ J.R. MILLER & SON DRUGGISTS PETERBORO, N.H.	Med	Rect	Cl	6 3/4	1 - 2
¶ JOHN R. MILLER PHARMACIST PETERBOROUGH, N.H.	Med	Ov	Cl	3 1/2	1 - 2
MINARD'S LINIMENT BOSTON	Med	Cyl	Cl	5 1/4	1 - 3
MINARD'S LINIMENT SO. FRAMINGHAM MASS. U.S.A.	Med	Cyl	Cl	5 1/4	1 - 3
MOOD'Y EXTRACT JAMAICA GINGER	Med	Rect	Aq	6 3/4	1 - 3
¶ MOUNT VERNON PURE RYE WHISKEY (F) THE COOK & BERNHEIMER CO. FULL QUART REFILLING OF THIS BOTTLE PROHIBITED (B) ONLY C&B CO. BOTTLING (Btm)	Liq	Sq	Amb	9 1/4	4 - 6
MT. WASHINGTON COLD SPRING MFG. CO. BOSTON, MASS.	Beer/ Soda	Cyl	Cl	8	1 - 2

WHISKIES, WATER AND SCHNAPPS. Unembossed dark amber whiskey flask, Mount Vernon Pure Rye Whiskey, Veronica Medicinal Spring Water, Unembossed amber schnapps.

EMBOSSING	TYPE	SHAPE	COLOR	HGT.	$ VAL.
¶ MOUNTAIN SPRING BREWING CO. REGISTERED (F) THIS BOTTLE NOT TO BE SOLD (B)	Beer	Cyl	Amb	9	3 - 5
MOXIE NERVE GOOD TRADEMARK REGISTERED (F) MOXIE (B)	Med	Cyl	Cl Aq	10	3 - 5
N. MURI & CO. LOUISVILLE, KY.	Liq	Rect	Amb	5 1/2	3 - 5
FRANK S. MURPHY GROCER 61 & 63 CHARLES ST. BOSTON	Liq/ Med	Rect Flsk	Cl	8 1/4	2 - 4
MURRAY & LANMAN DRUGGISTS, N.Y. FLORIDA WATER	Cosm	Cyl	Aq	9	2 - 4

N

EMBOSSING	TYPE	SHAPE	COLOR	HGT.	$ VAL.
NARRAGANSETT BREWING CO. PROVIDENCE, R.I. FAMOUS EXPORT LAGER REGISTERED (F) THIS BOTTLE NOT TO BE SOLD (B)	Beer	Cyl	Cl	9 1/2	2 - 4
NAUHEIM	Med	Ov	Cl	6	1 - 2
OTIS S. NEALE CO. (Mono OSN) HOWARD ST. BOSTON REGISTERED 1893	Soda	Cyl	Aq	9 1/2	1 - 3
NEOFERRUM	Med	Rect	Amb	7 1/4	1 - 2
A. NESTER AN TROY, NEW HAMPSHIRE REGISTERED	Soda/ Beer	Cyl	Cl	8 1/2	2 - 3

EMBOSSING	TYPE	SHAPE	COLOR	HGT.	$ VAL.
NEW MOUNTAIN SPRING BREWING CO. EXTRA FINE LAGER BEER WALPOLE, N.H. THIS BOTTLE MUST BE RETURNED TO THE BREWERY REGISTERED	Beer	Cyl	Cl	9 1/4	1 - 2
T. NOONAN & SONS BOSTON, MASS. (ST)	Cosm	Cyl	Cl	3 1/2	1 - 2

O
‾

EMBOSSING	TYPE	SHAPE	COLOR	HGT.	$ VAL.
THE OAKLAND CHEMICAL CO.	Hshld	Cyl	Amb	8 1/2	2 - 4
THE OAKLAND CHEMICAL COMP'Y (Mono CO) H_2O_2	Hshld	Cyl	Amb	7 1/2	2 - 4
OD CHEM. CO. NEW YORK	Hshld	Sq	Amb	6 1/2	2 - 4
ODIORNE'S (Mono ECCO) REGISTERED EQUAL TO IMPORTED MADE IN U.S.A. PORTLAND, ME.	Hshld	Cyl	Cl	8 1/2	1 - 2
OLD SMUGGLER GAELIC (Btm)	Liq	Cyl	OG	10	5 - 8
OMEGA OIL IT'S GREEN TRADE MARK THE OMEGA CHEMICAL CO. BOSTON, MASS.	Hshld	Cyl	Cl	6	1 - 3
ONE QUART	Med/Liq	Flsk	Cl	9 1/2	1 - 2
LIQUID OPOLDELDOC (OP)	Med	Cyl	Aq	4 1/2	3 - 5

EMBOSSING	TYPE	SHAPE	COLOR	HGT.	$ VAL.
PATRICK O'SHEA 303 MILLBURY ST WORCESTER, MASS.	Beer	Cyl	Cl	9	1 - 3
P					
¶ PAINE'S (F) CELERY COMPOUND (B)	Med	Sq	Amb	9 3/4	4 - 6
PA-PAY-ANS BELL ORANGEBURG NEW YORK, USA	Med	Rect	Amb	3	1 - 3
PA-PAY-ANS BELL	Med	Cyl	Amb	2 3/4	1 - 3
¶ PATENT	Med/Liq	Flsk	Amb	6	25-30
¶ PATENT	" "	Flsk	Amb	7 1/2	18-25
PEPTO-MANGAN (GUDE)	Med	6 Pnl	Aq	7	2 - 4
PETTS BALD EAGLE WHISKEY BOSTON MASS USA REGISTERED FULL QUART	Liq	Cyl	Cl	12 1/2	4 - 6
DR. J. PETTIT'S CANCER BALSAM	Med	Flsk	Cl	3 1/2	2 - 4
PETTY'S	Med	Ov	Cl	4	1 - 2
¶ PFAFF & HANSOM BOSTON	Soda	Cyl	Aq	7 1/2	3 - 5
PHENIX BOTTLING CO. DUFFY & CO. PHENIX, R.I. (F) THIS BOTTLE NOT TO BE SOLD (Bs)	Beer Soda	Cyl	Cl	9 1/2	2 - 4

EMBOSSING	TYPE	SHAPE	COLOR	HGT.	$ VAL.
THE CHAS. H. PHILLIPS CHEMICAL CO. NEW YORK	Hshld	Cyl	Aq	10 1/2	3 - 7
PIEL BROS. (Mono PB) EAST NEW YORK BREWERY (F) THIS BOTTLE NOT TO BE SOLD (B)	Beer	Cyl	Amb	9 1/2	2 - 4
DR. PIERCE'S FAVORITE PRESCRIPTION (F) R.V. PIERCE, M.D. (R) BUFFALO, N.Y. (L)	Med	Rect	Aq	8 1/4	2 - 4
DR. PIERCE'S GOLDEN MEDICAL DISCOVERY (F) R.V. PIERCE, M.D. (R) BUFFALO, N.Y. (L)	Med	Rect	Aq	8 1/2	2 - 4
LYDIA E. PINKHAM'S VEGETABLE COMPOUND	Med	Ov Flsk	Aq	8 1/2	2 - 4
¶ ED. PINAUD PARIS (Basket of Flowers) (F) ED PINAUD (Btm)	Cosm	Cyl	Cl	5	1 - 2
PIONEER BOTTLE CO. INC. 27 DOWNING ST. N.Y. (F) REGISTERED (Bs) 11 OZ. (B)	Beer Soda	Cyl	Aq	9 1/2	2 - 4
DR. S. PITCHER'S CASTORIA	Med	Rect	Aq	5 3/4	1 - 2
PLATT'S CHLORIDES THE HOUSEHOLD DISINFECTANT	Hshld	Cyl	Aq	9	1 - 3
¶ POISON	Med	Tri	Cob	3	3 - 5

INKWELLS AND INK BOTTLES. *Back row, left to right:* S. O. Dunbar, Taunton, Mass., Ward's, Carter's 77, Carter's, Unembossed ink. *Front row:* CPC, Square, Cylinder, Caw's, Clear mucilage.

EMBOSSING	TYPE	SHAPE	COLOR	HGT.	$ VAL.
POND'S EXTRACT (F) 1846 (Btm)	Med	Ov	Aq	5 1/2	2 - 3
PRESTON OF N.H. (Label reads "The Portsmouth Lavender Salt for the Traveller") (Ground glass stopper)	Cosm	Sq	Grn	3	3 - 5
PRESTON (F Bs) BOSTON (B Bs) (OP)	Med	Rect	Aq	5	3 - 5
PURE OLIVE OIL S.S.P.	Food	Long Neck Rnd	Cl	9, 9 1/2, 10 11 1/2	2 - 5
PUREOXIA REGISTERED BOSTON	Soda	Club	Aq	8 3/4	2 - 4
PURITAN (Mono PCCO) CARBONATING CO. MILLIS, MASS.	Beer	Cyl	SCA	9	2 - 4

R

RANDALL	Hshld	Cyl	Cl	5	1 - 2
RAWLEIGH'S BEEF, WINE & IRON (Label)	Med	Rect	Amb	8	1 - 3
M. REDDY & SONS 72 GERMANIA AVE. (F) JERSEY CITY N.J. (B)	Soda	Cyl	Aq	7 1/2	3 - 5
DR. ELIZABETH REED KEENE, N.H.	Med	Rect	Cl	4 1/2	1 - 2
REED & GARRICK N.Y. (Btm)	Med	Sq	Amb	5 1/2	1 - 3
REGISTERED FULL QUART	Med/ Liq	Flsk	Cl Aq	10	2 - 5

EMBOSSING	TYPE	SHAPE	COLOR	HGT.	$ VAL.
REGISTERED FULL 1/2 PINT	Med/ Liq	Flsk	Cl Aq	7	2 - 4
RELIANCE PHARMACY 346-348 CENTRAL AVE. ST. PETERSBURGH, FLA.	Med	Rect	Cl	3 1/2	1 - 2
RENNES (Mono) IT WORKS LIKE A CHARM (F) MAGIC OIL (L) PAIN KILLING (R)	Med	Rect	Aq	4 1/2	1 - 3
RENNE'S (F) MAGIC OIL (R) PAIN KILLING (L)	Med	Rect	Aq	6	1 - 3
REX DISTILLING CO. BOSTON (B) R. D. CO. Monogram FULL QUART (F)	Liq	Cyl	Cl	11 1/2	2 - 5
RHODE'S HAIR REJUVENATOR LOWELL, MASS.	Cosm	Rect	Amb	6 1/2	3 - 5
W. L. RICHARDSON'S (F) SOUTH READING (B) BITTERS (L) MASS. (R)	Bitt	Rect	Aq	6 3/4	15-20
ROBICHAUD & GAUTHIER (Embossed Beaver) GARDNER, MASS. THIS BOTTLE NOT TO BE SOLD	Beer	Cyl	Cl	9 1/2	3 - 4
RODERIC WILD CHERRY COUGH BALSAM	Med	Rect	Cl	5	1 - 2
¶ ROMOC CO. (R) ROMOC CO. SOLE PROP'S (L) BOSTON, U.S.A.	Med	Rect	Amb	7 1/2	4 - 6

EMBOSSING	TYPE	SHAPE	COLOR	HGT.	$ VAL.
RUBIFOAM FOR THE TEETH PUT UP BY E. W. HOYT & CO. LOWELL, MASS.	Cosm	Rect	Cl	4	1 - 2
RUMFORD CHEMICAL WORKS	Med	6 Panel	Grn	5 3/4	4 - 6
LOUIS P. RUPP PHARMACIST NINTH AVE. N. E. COR. 36TH ST. N. Y.	Med	Rect	Cl	6 3/4	1 - 3
S					
SAGWA (R) SAGWA (L)	Med	Rect	Aq	8 1/2	2 - 4
ST. JAKOBS OEL A. VOGELER & CO. BALTIMORE, MD.	Med	Cyl	Aq	6 1/2	2 - 3
SANFORD's 27 (Btm)	Ink	Cyl	SCA	2 1/2	2 - 4
SANFORDS JAMAICA GINGER THE QUINTESSENCE OF JAMAICA GINGER CHOICE AROMATICS & FRENCH BRANDY REGISTERED 1876 (F) POTTER DRUG & CHEM. CORP. (R) BOSTON, MASS, U.S.A. (L)	Med	Rect	Aq	6 1/2	1 - 3
SAUER'S EXTRACTS	Hshld	Rect	Cl	6	1 - 2
SAWYER'S CRYSTAL BLUEING	Hshld	Ov	Aq	6 1/2 8 1/2	1 - 2
SAXLEHNER BITTERQUELLE HUNYARDI JANOS (Btm)	Med	Cyl	Grn	9 1/4	4 - 6
DR. S.B.H.CO. 41 P.R. (Btm)	Med	Cyl	Aq	9	2 - 4

Cobalt Blue Inks and Poison Containers. Square ink, Two cylinder inks, Two S. S. Stafford inks, Spaulding, Two poisons, Amber ink.

EMBOSSING	TYPE	SHAPE	COLOR	HGT.	$ VAL.
GEO. SCHAEFFER PHARMACIST 895 GENESEE ST. BUFFALO, N.Y.	Med	Rect	Cl	4	1 - 2
SCOVILL (R) BLOOD & LIVER SYRUP (F) CINCINNATI, O (L)	Med	Rect	Aq	9 1/2	4 - 5
¶ SEVILLE PACKING CO. NEW YORK (Btm) (Insignia) (F)	Food	Cyl	Grn	6 7 1/2 9 3/4	4 - 8
J.T. SHEIM PHILAD	Cosm	Sq	Cl	4 3/4	1 - 2
SKILTON FOOTE & CO. (Bunker Hill Monument) BUNKER HILL PICKLES	Food	Cyl	Aq	5 1/2	2 - 4
¶ D & L SLADES BOSTON, MASS. (Btm) (Diamond & Fan pattern on Bs)	Food	Cyl	Cl	6 1/2	2 - 4
SLOAN'S N & B LINIMENT DR. EARL S. SLOAN BOSTON, MASS. USA	Med	Rect	Cl	6	1 - 2
SODERMAN & CO. (R) MINNEAPOLIS, MINN. (L)	Med	Rect	Aq	5 1/2	1 - 2
G.F. SOULET PHARMACIST MANCHESTER, N.H.	Med	Rect	Cl	5	1 - 2
¶ SPAULDING & CO. CHICAGO	Med	Tri	Cob	5 1/2	4 - 6
L. SPEIDEL & CO. REGISTERED (Mono LSCO) (Circle with leaf & B trademark) BOSTON, MASS.	Beer	Cyl	Cl	9	2 - 4
SPERM SEWING MACHINE OIL	Hshld	Rect	Cl	4 1/2	1 - 2

EMBOSSING	TYPE	SHAPE	COLOR	HGT.	$ VAL.
SPRINGFIELD BREWERIES CO. TRADE MARK (Mono SBCO) SPRINGFIELD, MASS.	Beer	Cyl	SCA	9	1 - 3
THE HOWARD W. SPURR SPECIALTY CO. BOSTON	Med	Rect	Aq	9	1 - 3
¶ S.S. STAFFORD INKS MADE IN USA	Ink	Cyl	Cob	6 7	4 - 8
¶ SUFFOLK BITTERS (R) PHILBROOK & TUCKER BOSTON (L)	Bitt	(Boar) Pig	Amb	4 x 9 3/4	100-150
¶ SUPERIOR HAIR OIL FOR THE TOILET (On label)	Cosm	Sq	Cl	5 3/4	2 - 4
T					
TAPPAN NEW YORK	Cosm	Cyl	Cl	3 1/4	1 - 3
TAPPAN'S GERMAN COLOGNE HERMAN TAPPAN, N.Y.	Cosm	Cyl	Cl	3 1/2	1 - 3
¶ JOHN THOMAS YONKERS N.Y.	Food	Sq	Aq	6 1/2	2 - 4
THREE IN ONE (R) 3 IN ONE OIL CO. (L)	Hshld	Cyl	Aq	5 1/2	1 - 2
TILDEN (Btm)	Med	Cyl	Amb	8	2 - 4
¶ DR. TOWNSEND^S (F) NEW. YORK. (L) SARSAPARILLA (R)	Med	Sq	Grn	10	20-30
TOURNADES KITCHEN (Btm)	Hshld	Cyl	Aq	5 1/2	1 - 2

EMBOSSING	TYPE	SHAPE	COLOR	HGT.	$ VAL.
TRICOPHEROUS FOR THE SKIN AND HAIR (F) BARRY'S (R) NEW YORK (L) DIRECTIONS IN THE PAMPHLET (B)	Med	Rect	Aq	6	2 - 4
TRUE CEPHALIC SNUFF BY THE KINGS PATENT	Med	Cyl	Aq	3 3/4	3 - 5
DR. TRUE'S ELIXIR ESTABLISHED 1851 DR. J.T.TRUE & CO., INC. AUBURN, ME. (F) WORM EXPELLER (R) FAMILY LAXATIVE (L)	Med	Rect	Aq	6	1 - 3
TRUE'S PIN WORM ELIXIR ESTABLISHED 1851 DR. J.F.TRUE & CO. AUBURN, MAINE (F) CLEARS THE BLOOD (L) KEEPS CHILDREN WELL (R)	Med	Rect	Cl	5 3/4	1 - 3
¶ TUTTLE'S ELIXIR CO. BOSTON, MASS.	Med	12 Panel	Aq	6	2 - 4
DR. S.A.TUTTLE (F) BOSTON, MASS. (B)	Med	12 Panel	Aq	6 1/4	2 - 4
U̲					
UNDERWOOD'S INK	Ink	8 Pnl	Aq	2 1/2	2 - 5
UNITED DRUG CO. BOSTON U.S.A. (Metal & cork cap Crown shaped inscribed Harmony of Boston)	Cosm	Rect	Cl	7	2 - 4
UNITED STATES MEDICINE CO. NEW YORK	Med	Rect	Aq	6	1 - 2

EMBOSSING	TYPE	SHAPE	COLOR	HGT.	$ VAL.
V					
VAN BUSKIRK'S (L) FRAGRANT SOZODONT (R) FOR THE TEETH AND BREATH (B)	Cosm	Rect	Cl	5	1 - 3
VAPO CRESOLENE CO. (F) PAT'D US JUNE 1895 ENG JULY 23 94 (L) (Hobnail pattern on 2 sides)	Med	Sq	Aq	4	2 - 5
¶ VERONICA MEDICINAL SPRINGWATER (Shld)	Med	Sq	Amb	10 1/2	4 - 6
VICHY ETAT	Med	Rnd	Grn	7 1/2	1 - 2
¶ VICI LEATHER DRESSING ROBT. H. FOERDERER PHILADELPHIA U.S.A.	Hshld	Sq	Aq	5	1 - 3
W					
¶ E. WAGNER TRADE MARK MANCHESTER, N.H. (F) THE PROPERTY OF E. WAGNER NOT SOLD (B)	Beer Soda	Cyl	Amb	9 1/2	2 - 5
¶ WALKER-GORDON MODIFIED MILK LABORATORIES (F) 1-8 Oz - 30-240 CC (B)	Food	Cyl	Cl	8	3 - 5
HENRY K. WAMPOLE & CO. PHILADELPHIA	Med	Rect	Cl	8	1 - 3
(#)¶ WARNER'S SAFE KIDNEY & LIVER CURE (Safe) (F) ROCHESTER, N.Y. (Bs)	Med	Ov	Amb	9 1/2	6 - 8

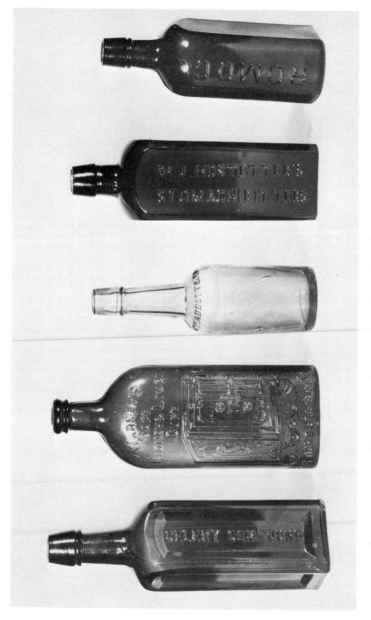

COMPOUNDS AND CURE-ALLS. *Left to right*: Paine's Celery Compound, Warner's Safe Kidney & Liver Cure, C. W. Abbott & Co., Dr. Hostetter's Stomach Bitters, Romoc.

EMBOSSING	TYPE	SHAPE	COLOR	HGT.	$ VAL.
¶ WEEKS GLASS WORKS (Btm)	Liq	Cyl	Amb	11	
WARRENTED FLASK	Med/Liq	Flsk	Cl	9 1/2	1 - 3
¶ WARRENTED FLASK	" "	Flsk	SCA	8	2 - 4
WARRENTED OVAL	" "	Flsk	Cl	9 1/2	1 - 3
PAUL WESTPHAL AUXILIATOR FOR THE HAIR NEW YORK	Cosm	Rect Flsk	Cl	8 1/2	2 - 4
WHITTEMORE BOSTON	Hshld	Rect	Cl	5	1 - 2
WHITTEMORE BOSTON (F) FRENCH GLOSS (B)	Hshld	Rect	Cl	4 1/2	1 - 2
WHITNEY MASON PAT'D 1858 (ST)	Food	2 Qt. Jar Cyl	Aq	9	3 - 6
WIGHTMAN'S EXTRACT	Hshld Cosm	Rect	Cl	4 1/2	2 - 4
MRS. WINSLOW'S SOOTHING SYRUP THE ANGLO AMERICAN DRUG CO. SUCCESSORS TO CURTIS & PERKINS PROPRIETORS	Med	12 Panel Cyl	Aq	5	2 - 4
DR. WISTAR'S BALSAM OF WILD CHERRY PHILADA IB (OP)	Med	8 Panel Cyl	Aq	6 1/4	4 - 8
WRIGHT'S INSTANT RELIEF	Med	Rect	Aq	5	1 - 2
WYETH (Btm)	Med	Rect	Amb	7 1/2	1 - 2
WYETH (Btm)	Med	Sq	Amb	9 1/2	1 - 2

EMBOSSING	TYPE	SHAPE	COLOR	HGT.	$ VAL.
WYETH (Btm) (Ground Glass Stopper)	Med	Cyl	Amb	2	3 - 5
JNO. WYETH & BRO. LIQ. EXT. MALT	Malt	Cyl	Amb	9	3 - 5
JOHN WYETH & BROS. PHILA (F)	Med	Ov	Cl	3 1/4 2 3/4	1 - 3
JOHN WYETH & BRO. BEEF JUICE	Food	Rnd	Amb	3 1/2	1 - 3
¶ Wyoming Catarrh Cure For the Relief and Cure of Catarrh Influenza Hay Fever, et. (On Label) (F) (Label gives Directions) (B)	Med	Rect	Cl	6	2 - 4
X					
¶ X˙ (Btm)	Liq	Case	OG	9	10-12
X (Btm)	Liq	Cyl	OA	11	4 - 8
X-ZALIA (Cattails) TRADE MARK BOSTON, MASS.	Cosm	Rect	Cl	7	2 - 3

DATA AND ADDENDA

G. O. BLAKE'S. We interpret the "S.O.B." inscribed on this bottle as a misprint for "G.O.B." A dealer in Vermont, however, has a saltier explanation!

BULLARD & FOSTER. This business was established in 1840 in Keene, New Hampshire. An 1885 Gazetteer lists them as, "pharmaceutists, dealer in drugs, medicines, fancy goods, and manuf. of Hammond's tonic bitters, Universal cough syrup, concentrated extract Jamaica ginger, saponacious camphorated tooth powder, Universal corn remover, etc., Hammond's cholera drops."

PERRY DAVIS PAIN KILLER. The bottle listed is a common find in New England. However, the photograph, page 36, shows a much earlier example with open pontil and perfect label dated 1852 and stating that the bottle could be returned to the manufacturer in Providence, Rhode Island for two cents credit!

T. M. DILLINGHAM'S. This bottle intrigues us as being most unusual and we have been unable to learn anything about it. The bottle appears to have been blown in a wooden mold, has a rough pontil, and a flange applied directly beneath the lip which has inside screw threads. We would be glad to hear from anyone with a similar bottle or having information regarding it. See photograph, page 19.

DORT & CHANDLER. This company was doing business in Keene, New Hampshire in 1885 as "pharmaceutists, dealers in drugs, medicines, fancy cigars, wallpaper, etc., manufs. of Clark's extracts of Jamaica ginger, and vegetable liver pills." See photograph, page 8.

O. LETTENMAYER. In 1885 he is listed as a Keene, New Hampshire dealer in fruits and confectionery, and manuf. tonic, birch, and ginger beer.

DR. LESURE. John G. Lesure was doing business in Keene, New Hampshire in 1885. He ran a livery, sale and exchange stable, and was a veterinary surgeon. It is said he bottled his liniment in large bottles for horses and small containers for humans!

WARNER'S SAFE CURE. The following is an excerpt from the local notes of *The Monadnock Monthly,* published in Jaffrey, New Hampshire, September, 1881. "Mr. Farnum has sufficiently recovered his health to be able to partially resume his labors. A few weeks ago, he was apparently at death's door, suffering from general prostration and kidney disease. He tells us that 'Warner's Safe Kidney and Liver Cure,' saved his life." See photograph, page 66.

BOTTLES ATTRIBUTED TO KEENE, N. H. *Above left:* Olive-green blacking bottle with open pontil. *Above right:* Deep aqua-marine octagonal ink. *Below left:* Olive-green snuff bottle with flat bottom. *Below right:* Three-part mold bottle.

Early New Hampshire Glassworks

SEVERAL EARLY GLASSHOUSES existed within a few miles of the authors' homes. Many pleasant hours have been spent exploring the original sites and researching old and new records concerning the products made by these companies. They include, in chronological order, Temple (1780), Keene (1814), Suncook (1839), Stoddard (1842), and South Lyndeboro, New Hampshire (1866). Although other glassworks operated throughout New England, only two, formerly located in Massachusetts, preceded the Temple glasshouse. While various later works operated contemporaneously with the New Hampshire glasshouses, many continued long after the South Lyndeboro Glass Company ceased operating in 1886. Innumerable books and articles have been written about these other New England glasshouses and are recommended reading for all serious bottle and glass collectors.

The first glass making venture in New Hampshire began in Temple, in 1780. It is almost impossible to attribute with any accuracy the glass manufactured here. The company was in operation so early and for such a short time—less than two years—that few records are in existence today. A small sign inscribed "Old Glass Site" marks the entrance to the secluded spot. An overgrown trail leads to the top of the mountain

Two FLASKS ATTRIBUTED TO KEENE, N. H. Rare half pint Masonic flask *(left)* is olive-amber with an open pontil. The larger flask *(right)* with eagle and olive branch is light amber with an open pontil.

"KEENE FLASKS", OTHER VIEW. The front side of the Masonic flask *(left)* showing Masonic emblem, and *(right)* the reverse of the large Eagle container with the familiar cornucopia design.

where only portions of the foundation and bricks from the early kilns remain as evidence of the short-lived experiment. Over the years, the area has been visited often by bottle and glass enthusiasts who have dug to great depths. It has now been closed to all digging. Before the closure, we visited the site several times and were able to excavate fragments of window-glass and a few sharp cullets of deep, greenish-aqua glass. We cannot relate these small shards to any bottle glass we have found, but they are treasured reminders of the first attempt to produce glass in New Hampshire.

In 1814 the first glass industry in Keene, New Hampshire commenced operations on what was formerly known as Prison Street, now Washington Street. The main output was window-glass. Glass making continued there until 1855 when the factory was destroyed by fire. The second and final glass industry in Keene was located on Marlboro Street. Wares produced in Keene ranged from purely utilitarian bottles to fine table-wares and decanters, three-mold inkwells to Masonic and historical flasks. The common colors associated with Keene are olive-amber, olive-green, and greenish-aqua, blue is extremely rare. The bottles on pages 70, 72 and 73, "Bottles attributed to Keene", have been carefully compared with other authenti-cated pieces. Since ours do not bear any positive identification marks, we have, through much study and research, attempted to classify them properly. The snuff bottle was found em-bedded, miraculously intact, in an old stone wall. It is deep olive-green with a perfectly flat bottom, no pontil, only swirls of glass indicating where it should be—a delightfully crude little bottle. The Masonic flask is a half pint, olive-amber, open pontil, with a sheared lip and was found buried beneath rocks and earth on a steep wooded hillside. It is considered a rare flask and an extremely lucky find! The flask displaying the eagle and olive branch is light amber with a sheared lip and open pontil. The crude little blacking bottle is olive-green, open pontil, and was found still retaining the cork-top applicator, in the partitions of an early home in the area.

From 1839-1850 the small village of Suncook, New Hampshire was the site of the third glassworks establishment to operate in New Hampshire. Aquamarine is the common color associated with this works. Window-glass and many off-hand pieces were made, most of which today are in the homes of the descendants of the early glassblowers, or in museums. Suncook glass is considered extremely rare.

While the above factory was operating in Suncook, a bottle factory was erected in 1842, in South Stoddard, New Hampshire. From this works and from a later glasshouse, located, in 1846, in "Mill Village", the much sought-after Stoddard wares were produced. All glass-making operations had gone out of business by 1873. Colors commonly associated with Stoddard are olive-greens, olive-ambers, and light ambers. The term "blood" amber is often used to describe the deep reddish amber in many of the later bottles produced here. The first and third flasks shown on page 76, "Bottles attributed to Stoddard", show hundreds of minute bubbles and many imperfections in the glass. They are deep amber, thin and delicate at the shoulders, tapering to a heavier base with an improved (round depression) pontil. The half pint flask has the word PATENT embossed on one side only, the color is a much darker amber and the glass is heavier throughout than those previously described. These were all found deeply

BOTTLES ATTRIBUTED TO STODDARD, N.
Unembossed light amber flask, "Pate
dark amber flask, Base of Weeks Gl
Works three-mold liquor bottle, "Pate
light amber flask, Three-part mold b
commonly known as a "Stoddard Stubb
Farley's Ink.

DIAGRAM OF BASE of Weeks Glass Wo
bottle, excavated in 1965 at Stoddard, N.

buried beneath dirt and firmly held intact by numerous tree roots!

The Weeks Glass Works bottle and the Farley's Ink (see opposite photograph) are considered rare Stoddard "finds", and are from the collection of Mr. George Chamberlain of Jaffrey, New Hampshire. Before acquiring the Weeks bottle, Mr. Chamberlain first purchased the broken base of a three-mold whiskey bottle, inscribed WEEKS GLASS WORKS (see at left), which had been excavated in 1965 from the former site of a glass-warehouse in South Stoddard. He later purchased the bottle shown in the photograph—a new find in Stoddard glass, of which we have located only two specimens. The small, eight-sided ink was commissioned by Farley's Store located in Marlow, New Hampshire, during the mid-1800's. This "gem" was found inside a pile of rocks, part of an old, tumbled-down stone wall!

The Lyndeboro Glass Company brought to a close the glass industry in New Hampshire. Commencing operations in 1866 and for a period of twenty years, workmen produced bottles and other containers in varying shades of aquamarine and the lovely Robin's-egg blue, commonly associated with this glasshouse. Some of the flasks produced here were embossed on the base, L.G.Co. Many of the early Mason canning jars and Moxie Nerve Food Tonic bottles can be attributed to this company.

Bottles which can be identified with any of these early glassworks are highly regarded by local bottle collectors and are eagerly sought by collectors all over the country. They create the greatest excitement and command the highest prices of any bottles found in this region.

Pricing Your Old Bottle

TODAY, all old bottles have a monetary value. To determine this value, factors such as age, color, shape, and rarity must be considered. The following clues will help to tell the age of an old bottle:

MOLD SEAMS run up each side of a bottle. Generally speaking, the nearer the lip, the newer the bottle.

THE PONTIL appears on the bottom of the bottle. A rough (or open) pontil would be earliest, with graphite pontil next in age.

WHITTLE MARKS (indentations giving a hammered appearance to the glass) indicate the bottle was blown in a wooden mold. Wooden molds were used previous to metal molds.

A SHEARED LIP is considered oldest with a sloppily applied lip next.

THE COLOR of glass has much to do with value of an old bottle. Red, amethyst (purple black) and blue seem to be the rarest colors. If your bottle is made of red glass, it need not be old to demand a high price. Blue ranges from pale, also called aqua, through a true blue (rare), to a cobalt or deep, bright blue. Amber will range from dark olive-amber through deep browns to reddish-brown and up to yellow. Green may appear almost as black and run up the spectrum through emerald to very pale shades which, in some instances, are considered aqua. Much of the differentiation among the numerous shadings of aqua lies in the eye of the beholder! The most common colors are clear and aqua. Due to their composition, certain types of clear glass will turn amethyst if exposed to the rays of the sun. This is called sun-colored amethyst and collectors derive pleasure and profit from it. All these colors and shadings eventually become meaningful to the bottle collector.

SHAPE is an important consideration. A fancy or figural bottle, even though of clear glass and not of great age, will often command a high price simply because of its shape.

RARITY must always be considered and is, perhaps, the biggest factor of all. Commemorative flasks and bitters bottles are at present more desirable than sodas or medicines. Locality influences rarity in some instances and what might be rare in New England could be common in another area.

The value of an old bottle is usually improved if it can be identified as having been manufactured in an early glasshouse.

The price-range given in the Tables of this book reflects the present market in the northeast and is based on personal observation and experience. Prices are, of course, subject to change. We believe prices to be higher in western and southern sections of the country. It is difficult to put an arbitrary price on a bottle since, in the last analysis, a bottle is never worth more than someone is willing to pay. This is a basic truth of any antique. If the demand is strong—price goes up. If interest wanes—prices drop.

If you sell your bottle to a dealer or at a flea market, (one of the most popular means of moving bottles in the east), the price you receive will necessarily be lower than if you are able to sell directly to the collector.

We feel strongly that bottles are "here to stay." We believe that old bottles should be classed as "antiques of tomorrow" which will, of course, incur the risk of constantly rising prices.

BIBLIOGRAPHY

Child, Hamilton. *Gazetteer of Cheshire County, N. H.* Syracuse, New York. 1885.

Dolan, J. R. *The Yankee Peddlers of Early America.* New York. 1964.

Griffin, S. G. *A History of the Town of Keene, N. H.* Keene, N. H. 1904.

Kendrick, Grace. *The Antique Bottle Collector.* Sparks, Nevada. 1963.

Knittle, Rhea Mansfield. *Early American Glass.* New York. 1927.

Leonard, Levi W. and Seward, Josiah L. D. D. *The History of Dublin, N. H.* Cambridge, Mass. 1920.

Maust, Don. *Bottle and Glass Handbook.* Uniontown, Penna. 1956.

McKearin, George S. and Helen. *American Glass.* New York. 1941.

McKearin, Helen and George S. *Two Hundred Years of American Blown Glass.* New York. 1949.

Putnam, H. E. *Bottle Indentification.* Jamestown, Calif. 1965.

Reed, Adele. *Old Bottles and Ghost Towns.* Bishop, Calif. 1961.

Tibbitts, John C. *Chips From the Pontil.* Sacramento, Calif. 1963.

Tibbitts, John C. *1200 Bottles Priced.* Sacramento, Calif. 1964.

Tibbitts, John C. *John Doe, Bottle Collector.* Sacramento, Calif. 1967.

Umberger, Art and Jewel. *It's a Bitters.* Tyler, Texas. 1967.

Watkins, Lura Woodside. *Cambridge Glass.* New York. 1930.

Watkins, Lura Woodside. *Antiques Magazine.* "Stoddard Glass." August, 1933.

WPA N. H. Writers' Project. *Hands That Built New Hampshire.* Brattleboro, Vt. 1940.